Oil Companies International Marine Forum

The Use of Large Tankers in Seasonal First-Year Ice and Severe Sub-Zero Conditions

First Edition - 2010

Issued by the

Oil Companies International Marine Forum

29 Queen Anne's Gate
London
SW1H 9BU
United Kingdom

First Published 2010

Book ISBN: 978-1-85609-429-0
eBook ISBN: 978-1-85609-430-6

Cover page photo courtesy of Neste Oil and Eeva Sumiloff

British Library Cataloguing in Publication Data
A catalogue record for this book is available from the British Library.

The Oil Companies International Marine Forum (OCIMF)

is a voluntary association of oil companies having an interest in the shipment and terminalling of crude oil and oil products. OCIMF is organised to represent its membership before, and to consult with, the International Maritime Organization and other governmental bodies on matters relating to the shipment and terminalling of crude oil and oil products, including marine pollution and safety.

Witherby Seamanship is a division of Witherby Publishing Group Ltd

Published in 2010 by
Witherby Publishing Group Ltd
4 Dunlop Square
Livingston,
Edinburgh, EH54 8SB
Scotland, UK

Tel No: +44(0)1506 463 227
Fax No: +44(0)1506 468 999
Email: info@emailws.com
www.witherbys.com

Printed and bound in Great Britain by Bell & Bain Ltd, Glasgow

Contents

List of Figures

List of Tables

Purpose and Scope

Independent ice navigation and the icebreaker-escorted navigation of large tankers are concepts that may be relatively new to many tanker owners and charterers. With the changes that have occurred in the Russian Federation, the tanker market has experienced an increase in the export of crude oil by large tankers from Baltic terminals impacted by the potential for winter ice navigation. This trend has continued elsewhere in the world as crude export terminals have been established or are planned in other ice navigation areas, such as the Barents Sea, White Sea and in proximity to Sakhalin Island (Eastern Russian Federation).

Some sectors of the industry have been used to dealing with the more traditional high ice class, smaller tankers designed specifically for escorted or unescorted ice transit. What is relatively new to the industry is the increase in demand for larger-sized crude tankers of low, or no, ice class to trade out of an increasing number of ports subjected to first-year ice formation.

The purpose of this publication is to provide guidance to chartering and vetting groups on the safe operation of tankers in areas affected by seasonal first-year ice.

Areas commonly affected by first-year ice include the Baltic Sea, White Sea, Barents Sea, the Eastern coast of Canada, Cook Inlet and in the proximity of Sakhalin Island in the Eastern Russian Federation.

The guidance is primarily aimed at the use of low, or no, ice class tankers, from 50,000 tonnes deadweight upwards, likely to encounter first-year ice. The document does not address established or specialised ice trades utilising high ice class tonnage.

It is recommended that charterers limit the use of low, or no, ice class ships in ice covered areas and non-winterised ships during severe sub-zero temperature conditions. For the purpose of this document, 'severe sub-zero' conditions are defined as forecasted daily mean ambient temperatures below -15°C.

Chartering groups will be aware of the different types of ice clauses in common use in charter parties. This document does not address the validity or otherwise of specific clauses and it is recommended that commercial or legal advisers are contacted for advice on such issues.

General guidance on the various national and regional ice navigation control services is contained in Appendix C.

The Use of Large Tankers in Seasonal First-Year Ice and Severe Sub-Zero Conditions

Ice Navigation Risk Assessment

Section

Many charterers and operators have a formal Hazard Risk Assessment process in place and conduct Hazard Risk Analysis when changes to activities lead to significantly higher risks or when circumstances create uncertainty over the safety of an operation.

It is, therefore, recommended that the operation of tankers in ice is subjected to a formal risk assessment process in accordance with individual company guidelines.

When considering chartering any vessel, including large crude tankers or ships with no, or low, ice class notation, for voyages that include the potential for independent ice navigation or icebreaker escort, it is recommended that charterers and operators conduct hazard risk assessments. The following are amongst issues that should be considered for risk prevention or mitigation:

- Ice class notation; winterisation class notation

- ice certificate

- appropriateness of insurance coverage in place due to breach of the Institute Warranty Limits (IWL). Ascertain limitations that may be described in individual charter parties or the ship's insurance

- double hull

- sufficient engine power available for use

- operational duration in propulsion machinery critical range (with particular reference to the harmonic constant of LNG membrane tankers)

- increased reserve bunkers and stores

- compliance with applicable rules and regulations

- use of Ice Advisors (particularly if the ice navigation experience of the bridge team is limited)

- assessment of ice and weather forecast services

- convoy strategy, including ship's position in convoy

- availability of icebreaker escort

- navigational risks in ice, including besetment

- cargo operations

- crew experience and training

- increased manning levels (particularly bridge team)

- additional UKC (allowance for ice accretion impact on draught and trim).

Appendix B contains examples of issues that may need to be considered when conducting a hazard risk assessment for operating in ice.

(Courtesy © Arno Keinonen)

Figure 1: Thick First-Year Ice

The Use of Large Tankers in Seasonal First-Year Ice and Severe Sub-Zero Conditions

Vetting for Ice Navigation

Section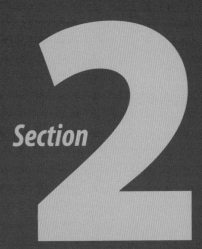

Depending upon the proposed trading areas, when intending to charter tankers for voyages where low temperatures, associated with ice navigation and/or icebreaker escort, are expected, it is recommended that the following basic issues relating to the ship's particulars or operating procedures are considered as part of the risk assessment process, particularly if the vessel is not ice classed or is of low ice class notation.

When considering a ship for a fixture, the intended voyage should be checked to determine if a breach of the Institute Warranty Limits will occur. If this is the case, appropriate action should be taken and the individual charter parties or, if applicable, ship's insurance, should be reviewed and arrangements made with the ship's owner or insurer, as appropriate.

It is important that the significance of the ice class notation is understood. Ice class notation alone does not automatically imply that the ship itself is suitable for commercial operations in extreme (cold) environmental conditions. The fact that the hull has an ice classification means that it has been constructed to incorporate the minimum required speed/power output in ice and has hull structural integrity that allows the ship to navigate in seasonal first-year broken ice up to classification limits. Beyond these limits additional measures, such as the use of icebreakers, will have to be taken.

'Ice classification' refers only to structural strength, propulsion power and arrangements. The fact that the hull is classed in this way gives no indication of the ship's suitability to operate in very low temperature environments. The recently-introduced optional 'winterisation' class notation provides an indication of the preparation of the ship to operate to an acceptable standard in extreme cold conditions, where icing of the ship can be experienced.

Reference should be made to Section 3 for further information on ice class notations and Section 5 for winterisation.

Chartering and vetting groups should ensure that ships intended for operations in extreme (cold) environments are capable and properly prepared. This includes the provision of adequate suitable equipment, preparations for equipment protection and procedures established to ensure safe operation and personnel welfare. OCIMF's Ship Inspection Report programme's database (SIRE) includes questions that specifically relate to the employment of vessels intending to trade in sub-zero conditions.

The following list outlines matters associated with ice navigation and/or icebreaker escort that should be considered when chartering ships for operations involving low temperatures. It is recommended that operators produce a suitable checklist to cover these requirements.

Classification

- Ice Class Notation

- Winterisation Notation.

Certification for Russian Ports

Ships entering Russian ports, or bound for Russian ports, may require an additional 'Ice Certificate' in accordance with local regulations. The process of obtaining the certificate includes assessment of a ship's suitability to operate in ice conditions and considers the following aspects:

- Ice performance, including ice class

- engine power, speed and manoeuvrability characteristics in ice

- compressive hull strength

- predicted ice conditions.

Charter Party/Insurance

- Hull and machinery insurance Institute Warranty Limits (IWL) should be checked

Crew Proficiency

- Do the Master and navigation officers have suitable experience of navigation in ice or operating in extremes of cold weather?

- Are navigating officers provided with basic ice navigation training?

Bridge Equipment

• Heated wheelhouse windows

• provision of equipment to assist with ice detection, e.g. high definition radars, infrared cameras

• searchlights - number, position, type, method of control, power and suitability for operation in ice and snow

• preferably enclosed bridgewings.

Figure 2: Inadequate Heating for Wheelhouse Windows

Hull

• Are systems in place to keep essential sea chests free of ice?

• Is steel suitable for exposure to low temperatures for voyage duration?

• Can propeller be kept sufficiently submerged below expected level ice conditions?

• Are accommodation heating systems adequate?

• Are systems in place to prevent freezing or snow blockage of essential air intakes and venting systems (including cargo and ballast venting systems)?

Procedures and Precautions

• Does the operator have procedures and/or precautions in place that include the following:

  ▫ Assessment of ice navigation and cold weather operational risks

  ▫ conduct of ice navigation/icebreaker escort navigation

  ▫ receipt of ice navigation information (e.g. ice charts, satellite images)

  ▫ cold weather operation and protection of, and access to, fire protection systems, life saving appliances, critical equipment and deck machinery, including mooring equipment

  ▫ prevention of freezing of services on exposed decks, including fire lines, air systems, control systems and instrumentation

  ▫ prevention of freezing of cargo and ballast systems, including ballast water and venting systems

  ▫ prevention of dangerous ice accretion

  ▫ provision of adequate cold weather clothing and personal protective equipment (PPE) for crew

  ▫ provision of suitable tools and materials for the prevention and removal of ice and snow on board?

The Use of Large Tankers in Seasonal First-Year Ice and Severe Sub-Zero Conditions

Commentary on Ice Class Notations

Section **3**

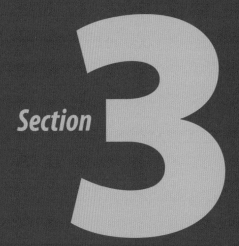

There is a wide range of ice class notations assigned by different Classification Societies and National Authorities. Ice classes cover different ship types and services, such as, cargo ships, icebreakers and tugs. For the purposes of this document, ice classes for tankers normally come under the banner of cargo ships intended for service in light ice to medium first-year broken ice conditions. Ice class requirements are based on structural strength, propulsion power and arrangements with regard to ice thickness. The different levels of ice class notations are defined according to the nominal operational ice thickness. The rules pertaining to ice class notations deal with:

- Hull reinforcement, e.g. 'ice belt' area from bow to stern between ballast and load water lines divided into forepart, amidships and aft parts.

- minimum engine power (linked to bow form of the ship), e.g. the Baltic regulations from the Finnish-Swedish ice class rules as applicable to ships built after 1st September 2003

- rudder reinforcement and fittings

- propeller, shaft and gears

- sea chests and cooling systems

- engine starting systems.

It should be noted that individual States or ports may require specific levels of ice class notation.

For further information on ice class notations, reference should be made to the appropriate Classification Society rules.

Most Classification Societies have their own individual ice class notation.

The following table provides information on the differing ice class notations used by Classification Societies. This information has been extracted from the Finnish Maritime Administration Bulletin No. 4/2.4.2007.

It should be noted that, when reviewing the data in the table, it is not always possible to determine direct equivalence between the various notations.

RS Russian Register**	GL	DNV	BV	LR	RINA	ABS	NK	Finnish/ Swedish Ice Class
LU5/ Arc5	E 4	ICE – 1A*	1A SUPER	Ice Class 1AS FS(+) Ice Class 1AS FS	1A Super	1AA	1A Super	IA Super
LU4/ Arc4	E 3	ICE – 1B	1A	Ice Class 1A FS(+) Ice Class 1A FS	1A	1A	1A	IA
LU3/ Ice3	E 2	ICE – 1B	1B	Ice Class 1B FS(+) Ice Class 1B FS	1B	1B	1B	IB
LU2/ Ice2	E 1	ICE – 1C	1C	Ice Class 1C FS(+) Ice Class 1C FS	1C	1C	1C	IC
LU1/Ice1	E	ICE - C	1D	Ice Class 1D	1D		1D	

** The Russian Register notation 'LU' was replaced by 'Arc/Ice' notations in 2007.

Table 1: Comparison Between the Ice Class Notations of Classification Societies
For ships, the keels of which were laid or which were at a similar stage of construction on or after 1st September 2003 (ref FMA Bulletin No.4/2.4.2007).

In 2007, the International Association of Classification Societies (IACS) published Unified 'Requirements Concerning Polar Class' (UR I). The requirements included Polar Class descriptions that are summarised in the following table:

Polar Class	Ice Description (based on WMO sea ice nomenclature)
PC 1	Year-round operation in all polar waters
PC 2	Year-round operation in moderate multi-year ice conditions
PC 3	Year-round operation in second-year ice, which may include multi-year ice inclusions.
PC 4	Year-round operation in thick first-year ice, which may include old ice inclusions
PC 5	Year-round operation in medium first-year ice, which may include old ice inclusions
PC 6	Summer/autumn operation in medium first-year ice, which may include old ice inclusions
PC 7	Summer/autumn operation in thin first-year ice, which may include old ice inclusions

Table 2: IACS Polar Ice Classes (Ref. IACS UR I1)

Note: the FMA Bulletin No.4/2.4.2007 states that, subject to the engine output of the ship, PC6 and PC7 may be considered locally as being equivalent to IA Super and IA respectively.

The Use of Large Tankers in Seasonal First-Year Ice and Severe Sub-Zero Conditions

Engine Power

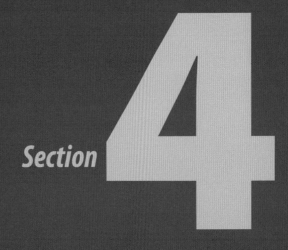

Section **4**

The engine power of ships operating in the Baltic has traditionally been governed by the Finnish-Swedish Rules with tables and mathematical formulae. These are predicated upon maintaining a minimum speed of 5 knots in broken first-year ice.

The majority of ships classified using these rules are less than 50,000 metric tonnes deadweight. As the size of ships being classified for ice navigation has increased up to and including Suezmax tankers of about 150,000 tonnes deadweight, other methodologies, such as ice model tests, have been used to provide evidence that this minimum speed requirement can be met with less power than that calculated using the formulae. The power requirement depends on the basic design, including hull and bow forms to reduce resistance to encountered ice, modification of power plant, propulsion and propeller design to achieve the necessary thrust and, hence, the ability to reach the minimum speed requirement.

The Use of Large Tankers in Seasonal First-Year Ice and Severe Sub-Zero Conditions

The Winterisation of Ships

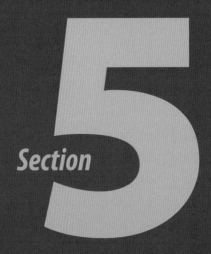

Section **5**

The ice class notation covers a ship's structural strength, propulsion power and arrangements. The notation does not cover suitability from the standpoint of commercial operability in low temperatures. Such operability is increasingly addressed by the use of a 'winterisation' notation, issued by Classification Societies. It should be noted that winterisation requirements are not bound to ice class and may be applicable to the ships without any ice class operating to ice-free ports where temperatures can be extremely low.

Some Classification Societies also use a 'de-ice' notation for vessels that operate in less severe climates. A vessel that is issued with a 'winterisation' notation will meet the requirements in place for a de-ice notation.

A Classification Society will consider the following elements before assigning a winterisation notation:

- The design service temperature, often defined as the lowest mean daily temperature for the area, requested by the ship operator

- the selection of material grades, for hull structures and equipment, which are suitable for the design air temperature

- ice accretion criteria for stability calculations. These are more demanding than for other ships as they consider the larger amount of ice that could accumulate on exposed hull parts

- adoption of means to maintain engine and accommodation space temperatures at acceptable values for the crew and machinery. Air temperature entering the engines is to comply with the requirements of the engine manufacturer

- sea inlet arrangements, to maintain them ice free

- adoption of anti-icing, de-icing and anti-freezing arrangements for equipment and onboard systems.

- the availability of suitable personal protective equipment (PPE), for use when working outside the accommodation areas.

Charterers or vetting departments should ensure that ship operators have written procedures addressing risk minimisation when preparing for, and operating in, cold weather and ice (refer Section 2).

The following provides guidance on matters that need to be considered when preparing a ship for operation in low temperatures. In the event that the nominated ship has a 'winterisation' notation, reference should be made to the details of the specific notation to determine the preparations that have been undertaken.

5.1 Cargo and Ballast Systems

Cargo System Valves

Prior to entering cold areas, all cargo, bunker, ballast and subsidiary valves that will be required to be used for operations should be inspected to ensure that their gearboxes contain no water and that they are well greased. A small amount of water in the gearbox of a hydraulic valve or in the valve bonnet will, when frozen, have a detrimental effect upon that valve and, in extreme cases, will render the valve inoperable.

Hydraulic cargo or Crude Oil Washing (COW) valves on deck should be protected with canvas covers and the valves should be frequently activated while in sub-freezing temperatures to avoid freezing/blockage.

If any valves are left 'cracked' open to avoid fracturing of valve bodies, it is recommended that each open valve is clearly marked, both locally and on the pipeline mimic diagram.

The condition of portable steam hoses and their connections on deck should be verified prior to use.

Figure 3: Ice Accretion on Supply Boat Manifold

Cargo Tank Pressure/Vacuum (P/V) Valves

It is strongly recommended that the P/V valves are thoroughly overhauled prior to entry into an area of sub-zero temperatures. While on passage valves should be protected from the effects of ice accumulation/accretion with canvas covers or steam heating. In extremely low temperatures canvas covers have been shown to be more effective than steam heating. However, it should be ensured that the presence of a canvas cover does not inhibit the effective operation of the P/V valve.

Before any cargo operation commences, it is recommended that any canvas covers are removed and that pressure/vacuum arrangements are checked to be free of ice blockage. In particular, it should be ensured that drain holes are clear and free to operate. Painting the seat faces of Hi-Jet valves with anti-freeze may assist in protecting them from freezing in the shut position and will prevent an ice film forming.

Inert Gas (IG) Deck Water Seal Heating

The deck water seal heating should be operational in freezing temperatures. It should be ensured that the inlet and outlet of the sealing water is not frozen and/or blocked by ice. Frequent checks should be undertaken to confirm a positive water flow.

P/V Breakers – Liquid (anti-freeze)

The deck breaker should be filled with anti-freeze (glycol as opposed to methanol based) as per the manufacturer's instructions. It is important that the correct concentration of ethylene glycol and water is used in the P/V breaker as excessive concentrations may not be effective, as illustrated in the following graph.

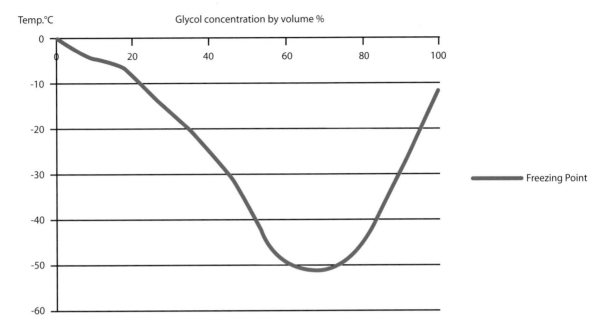

Frequent checks should be undertaken to ensure that the correct level is maintained in the breaker. Once clear of the cold weather, the density of the liquid in the P/V breaker will need to be tested and returned to the value necessary to ensure correct operation.

Mast Vent Riser (where fitted)

The mast vent riser valve should be protected with grease and a canvas cover. Flame arresters should be checked free of ice before the start of cargo operations. Prior to arrival, mast risers and inert gas (IG) lines should be drained of any liquid.

If fitted, automatic and manual valves on the IG main line and tank inlets should be kept greased and protected with canvas covers. The operation of piston breather valves on IG lines should be checked before operations commence and covers should be removed and de-icer sprayed in way of the valves.

It is recommended that the diameter of drainage lines on mast riser systems should be at least 50 mm.

Cargo Pumps

Deepwell Pumps

The motors and shafts of pumps located on deck should be protected with canvas covers to avoid delays caused by having to de-ice the pumps before discharging.

Submerged Hydraulic Pump Systems

The grade of hydraulic oil used in the submerged pump system will typically be suitable for operation in air temperatures down to minus 25°C, but its properties should be verified. The hydraulic system should be started on low load at least 30 minutes before the system is required for operations.

Some thickening of the hydraulic oil, due to the increased viscosity, may be experienced when ambient temperatures fall to zero and below. Minimising 'dead-legs' will assist in the pump's operation and, when initially starting the pump, it should be started very slowly to enable the warm hydraulic oil from the main to slowly displace the cold oil in the pump and consequently warm the pump through slowly. An increase in the normal loading may be placed upon the supply pump when starting a hydraulic pump, due to the change in viscosity of the hydraulic oil.

Cargo Stripping Systems

Any systems using water seal vacuum pumps need both the pumps and the seal supply header tanks to be protected from freezing. The manufacturer's recommendation should be followed and the required percentage of anti-freeze added to ensure safe operation.

COW and Tank Cleaning Systems

COW machine gearboxes should be protected with canvas covers. The gearbox oil should be renewed in order to avoid damage, particularly if the presence of any moisture is suspected. Tank cleaning lines should be drained of all water and isolated from the drive system. If tank cleaning is to be undertaken in cold regions, the sub-division of the cleaning system should be reviewed to limit the amount of pipework containing water. COW isolator valves should be drained of any water.

Cargo Tank Heating Coils

If not in use, heating coils and lines should be drained and blown through with air. To avoid 'dead-legs', steam delivery lines should be blanked off, preferably where they spur off from the main line.

Tank Cleaning Heater

When located in an exposed location, the tank cleaning heater will need to be protected and, in any event, should be drained.

Cargo Lines

Differences in temperature experienced by the ship can cause contraction of the deck lines that may not be taken up in the usual manner. There is a possibility of flange leakage and it would be prudent to check the integrity of the lines prior to use to ensure they are tight.

All cargo, ballast, tank cleaning and COW lines on deck should be well drained after their pressure testing or use. Particular attention should be paid to ballast systems, including ballast monitors and lines.

After loading, discharging or bunkering in cold climates, ship's lines should be drained and the drain valves left open until the ambient temperature rises sufficiently. Where possible, it is recommended that at least one tank filling valve is left open to allow the line to drain, thereby preventing the line from becoming pressurised due to temperature changes.

The pour point of the cargo being carried or to be loaded should be checked to determine whether line blockages may occur if cargo operations are stopped for any reason. Similarly, bunker fuel specifications should be checked for pour point.

Figure 4: Ice Accretion on Deck

Pump Rooms

Without compromising safety, pump room fans should be used only as required for ventilating the space to minimise the effect of sub-zero temperatures inside the pump room. Pump room doors should be kept closed, if possible.

Steam lines in the pump room, including those serving the tank-washing heater, should be drained down. If fitted, steam stripping pumps may be kept warming through if they are likely to be required for cargo operations or to provide some warmth in the pump room.

If fitted, pump room heaters should be turned on and, if provided on different floors, at least one on each floor should be used to promote convection currents in the space.

Oil Discharge Monitoring Equipment (ODME)

The fresh water supply to the ODME should be drained down together with the water supply/flushing pump.

Particular care should be taken when isolating and draining down the ODME as this is a well-documented source of failure or damage in cold climates.

Ballast Systems

Hydraulic ballast valves in empty tanks should be frequently activated to avoid freezing/blockage, unless other positive means are employed to prevent freezing.

Ballast tank vents may become frozen if not protected by canvas covers or steam heating on passage. However, to avoid the risk of over or under pressurisation of ballast tanks, the use of covers on vents should be strictly supervised to ensure that the vents can still operate as designed. It is recommended that any covers are removed prior to the commencement of operations. Frequent removal of any accumulated ice will be required.

Ice Accumulation in Ballast Tanks

Before entering cold climates, the Master should determine the density of the water contained within the ballast tanks. The more saline the water, the lower the freezing temperature will be. Consideration may be given to exchanging the ballast water to increase its salinity.

The surface of ballast water may freeze in ballast tanks. A considerable danger exists during de-ballasting operations should a layer of ice remain suspended in the tank, to fall at a later time, risking damage to internal structure and fittings. If possible, and if free surface stability calculations show it to be acceptable, ballast levels should be kept at or below the level of the sea surface. However, sea suctions should not be too close to the sea surface where there is increased risk of them getting blocked with ice.

Where fitted, ballast tank heating or bubbling systems should be in operation prior to entering areas with sub-zero temperatures, particularly when ballast levels are above the water line.

If stability and the ice belt depth allows and where no ballast tank heating or bubbling systems are fitted, periodic lowering and re-filling of the ballast may avoid the water's surface becoming frozen.

5.2 Deck

All void spaces, empty tanks, chain lockers and spaces should be sounded prior to entering cold weather. If any water is found, it should be educted dry, as far as is practical, to avoid ice damage when these residues freeze. The spaces should be regularly sounded to ensure that they remain water-free.

Sounding pipes, vents and remote gauges should be protected and remain operational as far as possible.

As well as the natural consequences of sub-zero temperatures, e.g. freezing of liquids, another area that should be managed is the accumulation of ice on deck from freezing spray and rain. Consequently, many of the actions below relate to covering equipment with canvas, heavy-duty plastic sheet or similar material. Ice accumulations on unprotected equipment will render the equipment inoperable.

Tank gauging/dipping point valves should be covered to prevent ice accumulation. Similarly, cargo manifold pressure gauge connections should be covered.

Cargo manifold drip trays should be maintained dry. The drain valves on the drip tray should be drained of any water to prevent them freezing in sub-zero temperatures.

Cargo handling cranes and derricks should be operated and tested prior to the vessel entering sub-zero temperatures. The operation of any heating arrangements provided, for example, in crane cabs, should also be confirmed.

The pneumatic or electrical motors used for raising or lowering accommodation ladders should be adequately covered to prevent ice accretion.

Action should be taken to prevent scupper holes from becoming iced over, thereby making it difficult for plugs to fit correctly. Coating of the scupper plugs' rubber faces with petroleum jelly may prevent seizure of the plugs in scupper holes.

The main air valve to deck should be closed and the airline drained down, taking care to remove any moisture that may be contained within the line, particularly at the ends. If air has to be supplied to deck, an air drier should be used.

Deck Equipment

With hydraulic equipment, such as winches and hose handling cranes, particular attention needs to be paid to the operating temperature range of the hydraulic fluid.

Control boxes and motion levers should be protected by canvas covers.

For hydraulically driven systems, oil should be circulated continuously when the external temperature is below 0°C to ensure that the fluid systems are maintained at working temperatures. If this is to be achieved by leaving machinery (e.g. winches) running, careful attention should be paid to the regular lubrication of the equipment. The oil manufacturer's stated operating temperature range/viscosity should be checked for suitability. Oils may have to be treated with an appropriate viscosity additive or, in extreme cases, the oil may have to be changed for a more suitable grade.

Mooring wires and synthetic ropes should be protected by canvas covers to stop ice accretion until they are required for use. Ice crystals can form within unprotected ropes and can cause damage to the rope's fibres.

Ice Accretion on Windlasses

Due to their exposed location, windlasses and winches are likely to be subjected to heavy ice accretion. Prior to arrival in port, winches and windlasses should be proven to be operational and additional time may have to be allowed to clear any ice accretion. In addition, both anchors should be lowered to prove that they are free to run from the pipe (i.e. not frozen in) when safe navigation permits. However, the anchors should be brought fully home prior to mooring.

Figure 5: Ice Accretion on Deck Machinery

Other

Particular care should be taken in sealing the chain locker, spurling and hawse pipes.

Sprinkler systems should be drained down free of water. This should include sprinkler systems to chemical, paint and other store rooms, mast riser systems and any fresh or salt water systems covering other spaces.

5.3 Engine Rooms, Machinery and Systems

Prior to entering cold weather areas, the engine room should be prepared for the anticipated conditions. Particular consideration should be given to deciding when the engine room should be manned.

The provision of heaters in the engine room/machinery spaces will assist in maintaining temperatures above freezing. The use of hot-air-blown space heaters may also be considered within these spaces.

The following points should be considered to maintain the safe and effective operation of the ship's propulsion and ancillary systems.

Cooling System Intakes (Sea Chests)

The maintenance of effective cooling arrangements is a prime consideration in sub-zero sea temperatures. It is important that all seawater strainers are cleaned since a clogged filter will lead to reduced flow, resulting in rapid ice formation within the strainer.

Particular care should be taken to ensure that the heating arrangements of the cooling water sea chests are working at optimum efficiency. Steam heating systems to sea chests should be checked to confirm their good working condition and be operated continuously when the ship is in ice infested waters.

Consideration should also be given to the following:

• The risk of damage to the engine as a result of severely overcooling the jackets

• optimising the number of coolers in service

• raising cooling temperatures

• adjusting charge air coolers

• monitoring the scavenge temperatures to ensure that they are maintained within limits.

When re-circulating cooling systems are fitted, the correct levels of cooling water should be available before entering sub-zero conditions and the condition of all valves and pumps should be verified. The system should be placed in service before entering ice conditions.

Fuel Systems

It should be ensured that heating systems are operating on all bunker storage tanks, bilge tanks, bilge overflow tanks and main engine sump settling and service tanks. Bunker storage tank temperatures should be kept at least 5°C above the minimum transfer temperature given in the fuel's specification.

Consideration should be given to changing over from heavy fuel oil to diesel oil prior to closing down the main engine so that the fuel lines are primed with diesel oil instead of fuel oil. This ensures that any cooling of fuel lines will not result in oil solidifying within the lines.

Cargo Pumps

If steam pumps are fitted it should be ensured that cargo pump steam inlet lines are completely drained of condensate to avoid damage to pipe work.

Cargo pump lube oil priming pumps should be run to ensure that the lubricating oil remains at a satisfactory temperature and does not become too viscous.

Stern Tube

Stern tube oil should not contain any free water or be contaminated with water/oil emulsion. Consideration should be given to draining any water from the system or replacing the stern tube oil charge.

It is recommended that stern tube bearings and seals located outside the hull are designed not to leak pollutants. In this context, non-toxic biodegradable lubricants are not considered to be pollutants.

The temperature of the stern tube cooling water tank should be closely monitored. Consideration should be given to sourcing a suitable additive or temporarily draining the tank when the contents approach 0°C.

Ventilation

Consideration should be given to stopping all but one main engine room ventilation fan to maintain a reasonable ambient temperature in the machinery space. However, suitable air flow should be maintained to allow the correct operation of boilers, main and auxiliary engines if they are not provided with separate ducting.

It should be ensured, so far as possible, that vents feeding off the main ventilation system do not blow directly onto fuel lines or pipes containing fuel oil or onto heavy fuel oil transfer pumps.

Ventilation fans in the steering gear space should be stopped and vent flaps closed to maintain a reasonable ambient temperature.

Accommodation heating systems should be activated and a comfortable temperature and humidity maintained in accommodation spaces.

Pneumatic and manual fan flaps should be regularly operated to ensure their correct operation and to prevent freezing/seizing.

Hydraulic Machinery

Hydraulic pumps should be regularly run to maintain the temperature of the oil and machinery.

Electrical Systems

Trace heating tape is an adhesive tape with wire contained in it that can be used to heat pipes and machinery. It comes with the necessary documentation to calculate current, load and wattage. It provides a temporary, quick and cost-effective solution to heating pipes and machinery. If the tape is to be used in hazardous areas, it should be appropriately rated for such use.

Generators

The fuel temperature of any generator running on diesel or gas oil should be monitored and arrangements made for temporary local heating if the temperature approaches the fuel's cloud point.

Emergency Generators

The emergency generators on some ships have electric heating on the alternator end. This should be tested to ensure its satisfactory operation.

The emergency generator room external vent flaps and supply fan damper should be kept closed. Notices advising of the status of the flaps and dampers should be posted in the emergency generator room and main engine control room. It should be ensured that the emergency generator's cooling water contains the correct amount of anti-freeze.

Emergency Batteries and Battery Lockers

Emergency batteries and power for communications equipment should be protected from extreme low temperatures. Spaces containing batteries may need to be provided with space heaters, depending on their location/exposure.

General service batteries are unlikely to freeze in expected conditions but, as a precaution, they can be covered with plastic sheet.

Water

When not Generating Water

Domestic/Distilled Tanks. Where possible, gauge glasses to these tanks should be drained. If gauge glasses are not drained there is a possibility that the lower section of the gauge glass will become frozen and shatter. Remote sensing gauging cannot be relied upon.

If the evaporator is not in use, lines to the storage tanks should be drained.

When Generating Water

The temperature of the water in the storage tanks should be monitored and water made to the tanks as necessary to maintain a reasonable temperature. As the distillate from the evaporator is at about 50°C, it should prevent the water in the tanks becoming cold enough to freeze.

The supply lines from domestic fresh water tanks to pressurising pumps are generally susceptible to freezing, depending upon their location, and appropriate precautions should be taken.

Boiler water sensing lines should be protected from freezing

Compressed Air

If ice contaminates the general service and/or instrument air system, there is a possibility of problems with the onboard instrumentation air supply. It is recommended that driers are fitted to all air systems.

Steering Gear

Steering gear motors should be kept running at all times to keep the oil warm. Space heaters should be used in the steering flat to ensure that the equipment is maintained at a satisfactory temperature. The use of heaters in the steering flat may result in significant condensation forming on deckheads and bulkheads so equipment may have to be protected from condensate dripping from these surfaces.

Lubricants and Oils

It should be ensured that only oils and greases are used that are suitable for the anticipated temperature.

Diesel Oil Blends

Diesel oil may be blended with kerosene to depress the pour point, as indicated in the table below:

Ratio Diesel/ Kerosene	Pour Point °C
50 : 50	minus 14°
40 : 60	minus 18°
30 : 70	minus 23°

It should be noted that, as the proportion of kerosene is increased, the lubricity of the blend will be reduced and machinery may require more frequent checks and maintenance. In addition, it should be ensured that the flash point of the final blend conforms with IMO regulations.

5.4 Safety and Life Saving Equipment

Periodic inspections of all safety-related systems should be undertaken during the exposure to extreme temperatures to ensure the effectiveness of the precautions being taken.

All available space heaters and engine sump heaters and/or heat lamps should be fully utilised. Ships that do not regularly trade in such conditions may require additional equipment to be supplied.

Survival Craft

All life rafts should be rated for safe operation according to the environmental conditions likely to be experienced.

Ice accretion should be regularly removed from the life rafts, cradles, cradle release pins and launching equipment to retain their preparedness for launching and inflation.

Similar precautions should be taken for lifeboats, rescue boats and their launching appliances. Particular checks should be made to ensure that brake release securing pins are free to be extracted.

An ice removal mallet should be readily available in the vicinity of survival craft. Care should be exercised when using mallets to avoid permanently damaging any equipment.

The overall condition of the gel coat of lifeboats should be inspected for any damage, particularly penetration of the gel coat and fibre sub-structure, in good time prior to entering the cold zone. Repairs should be undertaken in a warm dry climate to limit water ingress, which, if subjected to freezing, can cause severe damage to the boat's structure.

Lifeboat Engines

Lifeboat engines should at all times remain available for immediate use and be capable of starting within two minutes in the environmental conditions likely to be experienced.

The process of starting an extremely cold engine is quite different from normal starting procedures. The correct procedure should be drawn to the attention of all persons likely to be involved in starting the engine in very cold conditions to ensure they are familiar with the operation.

Manufacturer's instructions for the grade of oil to be added to the cold starting pots, if fitted, should be followed. This oil should be readily available in the lifeboats. It should be borne in mind that in cold conditions the performance of the starting batteries might be diminished.

If fitted, heaters in lifeboat engines should be used. Consideration should also be given to fitting trace heating around the doors of enclosed lifeboats to ensure that they do not freeze in the closed position.

Lifeboat Fuel Systems

An appropriate grade of diesel or gas oil should be used to prevent waxing in fuel systems leading to lack of engine start and impaired reliability. When replacing the fuel grade, lifeboat fuel tanks and the fuel line contents should be changed out and the engine run on the new fuel to ensure that the system is properly flushed and primed.

Lifeboat Cooling Water Systems

The lifeboat cooling system, if of a recirculating self-contained type, should be adequately protected with an anti-freeze solution. If the system is not self contained it should be checked to ensure that no obstructions or contamination prevent the natural drainage of the system.

Lifeboat Water Spray Systems

The spray systems, including pumps, on the lifeboats, should be drained of water. In some classes of boat, if the spray pump is frozen it will inhibit starting of the lifeboat engine by locking the propeller shaft.

Lifeboat Water Rations

Precautions should be taken to avoid the freezing of water rations stowed in lifeboats.

Stern Launched Lifeboats

It is not safe to free-fall release a stern launched lifeboat onto ice. It will be necessary to break the ice, either by judicial use of the ship's engines or by other craft. The lifeboat may be winched out and down to rest upon the ice surface.

Rescue Boats with Water Jet Engines

The rescue boat should be maintained in a condition that will allow immediate use but will also protect the boat from the extremes of weather.

Subsidiary LSA Equipment

Immersion Suits

Commonly supplied immersion suits have a design operational range in immersed (seawater) temperatures from minus 1.9°C up to 35°C. Immersion suits are available that have enhanced insulation properties.

TPAs (Thermal Protective Aids)

TPAs should be effective within a temperature range appropriate to the temperatures likely to be encountered.

Lifebuoys

It should be ensured that lifebuoys are not iced into position and are free to be removed and used.

External Pyrotechnics

The release pins for bridge wing lifebuoys/smoke floats should be well greased to ensure their proper operation.

EPIRBs

EPIRBs should be maintained ice-free.

Breathing Apparatus and Oxygen Therapy Units

In sub-zero conditions, the use of compressed air/oxygen breathing or resuscitation apparatus should be considered with care. The hazards involved include the freezing of the demand valve and exhale valve due to the freezing of exhaled vapours from the user leading to premature emptying of the gas bottle or failure of the system. The effect of low temperature (below minus 4°C) on the lungs of the user, can lead in protracted cases to frostbite of the lung tissue.

Eye Wash Stations

Eye wash fluid is typically effective in a fluid temperature range of 5°C to 25°C. Below 5°C the effectiveness of the fluid may be reduced. At 0°C fluid temperature, it is recommended not to use the fluid except in cases of extreme urgency as it may cause damage to the eye. Consideration should be given to temporarily withdrawing exposed eyewash stations into the accommodation while the vessel is operating in sub-zero conditions.

Hard Hats

The safe operating temperature range for hard hats is marked within the hat by the manufacturer. Some hard hats are certified for safe operation to minus 40°C and their use should be considered.

5.5 Fire-Fighting Systems and Equipment

Fire extinguishing systems should be designed or located so that they are not made inaccessible or inoperable by ice or snow accumulations or low temperatures.

Equipment, appliances, systems and extinguishing agents should be protected from freezing and the minimum temperatures anticipated for the voyage.

Precautions should be taken to prevent the nozzles, piping and valves of any fire extinguishing system from becoming clogged by impurities, corrosion or ice build up.

The exhaust gas outlets and pressure/vacuum arrangements on gas detection systems should be suitably protected from ice build up that could interfere with the system's effective operation.

Water or foam extinguishers should not be located in any position that is exposed to freezing temperatures. These locations should be provided with extinguishers capable of operation under such conditions.

General guidance on typical operating temperatures for portable extinguishers follows. Operators should check the actual performance limitations of extinguishers by referencing manufacturer's data.

Water, Gas and Low Expansion Foam

Fire extinguishers located in exposed areas are susceptible to freezing. Foam extinguishers will be ineffective and, when they do thaw out, the foam compound will have been 'frost damaged', rendering them useless.

Unprotected Foam and Water Extinguishers

Unprotected foam and water extinguishers are rated for safe and effective operation to 1°C. If protected with ethylene glycol, this figure may be revised downward to minus 10°C.

If an additive is used, it may enable water and foam extinguishers to be operable at temperatures down to minus 20°C.

CO_2 Extinguishers

CO_2 extinguishers are typically rated for safe and effective operation to minus 20°C. However, if operated at these temperatures extreme caution should be taken to avoid contact with any part of the extinguisher or expelled gas to avoid low temperature burns.

Dry Powder Extinguishers

These types of extinguishers are typically rated for safe operation from minus 30°C to 60°C. The extinguishing medium presents no additional special precautions. However, the propellant, CO_2 needs to be treated with caution to avoid personnel injury through exposure to the cold gas.

AFFF

AFFF (Aqueous Film Forming Foam) extinguishers typically have a nominal safe operational range of temperatures between 5°C and 60°C.

Fire and Foam Systems Hoses and Nozzles

Most hoses are typically rated for safe operation at temperatures down to minus 20°C and nozzles to minus 25°C. Cold weather hoses are available that are rated to minus 40°C and are marked accordingly.

Fire and Foam Lines

The fire and foam lines on deck should be well drained and maintained ready for immediate use at all times. Monitors, hydrant valves and any other moving parts should be well greased and protected by canvas covers to avoid ice/snow accumulation that may prevent their immediate operation. Their movement should be regularly checked to ensure that they remain free.

The pipework serving water curtains and spray systems should be checked drained and empty.

To avoid any 'dead-legs', any items drawing water from the fire main, such as hawse pipe cable washer lines, should be drained, particularly if a re-circulatory fire main line is in use.

The storage locations of fixed foam system bulk storage tanks may need heating to ensure that the temperature in these spaces remains above zero. Consideration may have to be given to using temporary space heaters to maintain an adequate temperature.

Portable Foam Equipment

Drums and canisters of foam for portable branch pipe appliances are subject to the same considerations as portable fire extinguishers.

Fire Hose Boxes

The catches, locks, dogs and hinges on fire hose boxes should be kept ice-free. Spray nozzles and couplings should be well greased and water free. All hoses should be completely drained of water to avoid damage and to facilitate their rapid use.

5.6 Pollution Prevention and Response

Prevention of pollution to the environment in areas of extreme environmental sensitivity is of great importance. Care should be taken to follow all regulations in force and particular to the areas the ship is trading in. An example of local requirements is that which refers to the prevention of grey water discharges.

Ship's oil spill response procedures should be reviewed to ensure that they take due account of issues associated with operations in ice and/or cold temperatures.

It should be ensured that pollution response arrangements are not compromised by the effects of ice accretion. If pollution response equipment is normally stored forward consideration should be given to relocating it in the after part of the ship, where the possibility of icing is less.

The ship's sewage system should be in good operating condition and suitable storage available in the event that discharge to sea is not permitted by local regulation.

5.7 Ice Accretion and Snow Accumulation on Ships

Ice accretion and snow accumulation poses hazards for personnel having to work onboard the ship, as well as to the ship itself. De-icing a ship is a complex, time-consuming and hazardous operation. Efforts should be taken to minimise, as much as possible, sea spray on deck by either reducing speed and/or altering course. It should be borne in mind that ice accumulation also results in a potential for falling ice and the associated dangers.

(Courtesy © Arno Keinonen)

Figure 6: Danger Posed by Falling Ice

In certain conditions, ice formed of fresh water or sea water accumulating on the hulls and superstructures of ships can pose a serious hazard. Fresh water ice can form from fog, drizzle, rain or snow. Icing from seawater is generally experienced with air temperatures of below minus 2°C and in conditions of strong winds.

Where deck icing is evident, additional care needs to be exercised when moving and working around the ship, remembering that ice can be found both on the external surfaces and, in some conditions, in internal spaces.

This section describes the effects of ship icing and how best to avoid or mitigate its formation and impact.

Description of Sea Spray Icing

Sea spray icing is a serious hazard for marine operations. The effects of icing may impede the ability to conduct operations in a safe and timely manner.

Causes

Sea spray icing occurs when wave-generated spray comes into contact with cold exposed surfaces and the air temperature is below freezing. There are two general factors to be considered, 'environmental' and 'ship characteristics' and these are briefly described below.

Environmental Factors

The following environmental factors contribute to ship sea spray icing:

- Wind speed, e.g. typically above 18 knots or 9 m/s but sometimes lower

- air temperature, e.g. below freezing (minus1.9°C for salt water)

- water temperature, e.g. below 7°C

- freezing temperature of water

- wind direction, relative to the ship

- swell and wave characteristics

    □ Wave size

    □ wave length

    □ wave propagation direction.

Ship Characteristics

In addition to the above environmental factors, the severity of sea-spray icing depends on ship characteristics. Some ship factors to consider:

- Speed

- heading (with respect to wind, waves and swell)

- bow design

- length

- freeboard

- cold soaking.

Figure 7: Effects of Icing and Ice Accretion

When a ship has been in cold temperatures for a long time, e.g. two or three weeks, the body of the ship will remain cold even if the air temperature is warmer. This 'cold soaking' may result in icing being more severe than expected given the current environmental conditions.

The graphs below illustrate sea spray icing potential as a function of wind speed and air temperature for a given sea temperature. Generally, icing is not a problem at sea temperatures greater than 7°C, and no cases with higher temperatures were considered when the algorithm was derived.

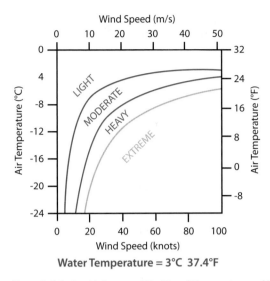
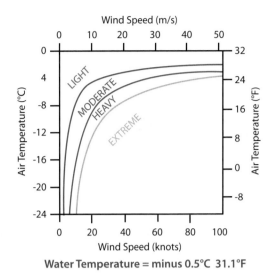

Figure 8: Relationship between Wind Speed, Temperature and Icing
Source: Overland, J.E., 1990: Prediction of vessel icing at near-freezing sea temperatures.

Note: Figure 8 provides only an approximate guide for ships steaming into the wind and waves. The actual potential for icing depends on the type, load, and handling characteristics of a particular ship. Masters and bridge watchkeepers should be well aware of the wind speeds which cause sea spray to reach the deck and superstructure and should base their assessment on the potential for icing on this knowledge.

The Use of Large Tankers in Seasonal First-Year Ice and Severe Sub-Zero Conditions

Navigation of Large Tankers in Ice

Section 6

Large conventional tankers are normally designed for optimum performance in open water. This applies to designs for hull form, rudders and propellers. Large conventional tankers perform relatively poorly in ice for a number of reasons, including:

- They are more difficult to manoeuvre

- propellers designed for optimum open water performance may not be suited for delivering maximum thrust in ice

- propellers and rudders designed for open water operation may be more susceptible to ice impact damage.

Given the above, it is recommended that the propeller is kept as deep as possible and it should always be deeper than the thickness of level ice to be navigated. The speed of the ship should be controlled to reduce the risk of ice damage. However, large tankers may find that, once stopped in ice, regaining momentum is difficult without icebreaker assistance.

'Besetment', or getting stuck in ice, is a risk that the Master of a large tanker should be aware of when navigating in ice. Ice under pressure can cause local forces on the ship's hull that may result in damage to plating, structure or hull coatings.

Masters should avoid sailing too close to an ice edge, particularly during rough weather. Sections of the ice edge are liable to break off and be energised in the waves, creating a danger to ships as they may impact a vessel above an ice strengthened belt, risking significant damage.

The waterline coating systems of tankers may suffer heavy abrasion damage in ice. In addition, some impact deformation of hull plating is possible. Charterers may wish to consider arranging independent inspections of the hull before and after ice voyages.

Where ship's officers and crew are not particularly experienced, the use of an Ice Advisor may be considered to supplement onboard knowledge.

In the 1990s a new type of ice-class tanker was developed that was designed to break ice when moving astern. The tankers are provided with azimuth propulsion systems, which comprise of one or two propulsion units, which generally rotate through a full 360° circle.

6.1 Icebreaker Escort of Large Tankers

Note: for the purposes of this Section, the following definitions apply:

Escort means any ship with superior ice capability in transit with another ship.

Escorted operation means any operation where a ship's movement is facilitated through the intervention of an escort.

Icebreaker means any ship whose operational profile may include escort or ice management functions, whose powering and dimensions allow it to undertake aggressive operations in ice-covered waters.

Charterers should be aware that large tankers are likely to require icebreaker assistance. The icebreaker escort of large tankers is not a subject that can be easily condensed. However, for the purposes of this document, it is considered useful to provide some basic information.

There are various different types, designs and sizes of icebreakers. Icebreakers used for escorting large tankers may be multifunctional or may have been designed with other primary or secondary purposes in mind. The world's icebreaker fleet is ageing and it is recognised that there is a shortage. Most escort systems work on the principle of providing icebreaker assistance only when the ship is bound to the port/country that also provides the icebreaker service.

In general terms, large conventional tankers may require icebreaking assistance in anything more than thin unbroken ice. The ice channel required by large tankers will usually be wider than the beam of the icebreaker. Two icebreakers may be required for efficient escort. However, depending on the circumstances, single icebreaker escort is also possible.

Figure 9: Icebreaking Support Vessel

There is a range of different large-ship icebreaker escort techniques in use depending, for example, on the ice conditions, preferred methods of the local icebreaker Captains and availability/design of icebreakers. Conventional, high powered icebreakers can achieve wider ice channels than their beam by breaking thin or medium thickness ice at high speeds of advance by using the wake generated.

A common mode of large ship escort operations consists of two icebreakers in tandem (one ahead of the other) and separated transversely by about 20 metres (depending on the beam of the tanker). This provides an ice channel approximately the width of the combined beams of both icebreakers plus the separation distance. The tanker travels at a 'safe distance' behind the nearest icebreaker at a 'safe speed' nominated by the icebreaker Captain, who controls and manages the convoy. The tanker will encounter ice floes in the channel, as illustrated in Figure 10.

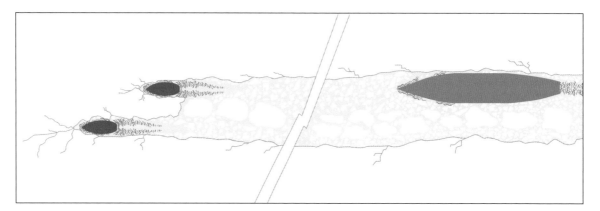

Figure 10: A Method of Large Ship Escort in Ice

When ships are in a convoy, either directly following an icebreaker or when following another ship, Masters must be alert to the danger of collision between their own ship and the icebreaker or other ships in the convoy, particularly if the icebreaker or vessel ahead comes to a sudden stop due to ice ridges, deformed ice or extreme ice pressure.

A following tanker may miss the ice channel when navigating from open leads or nilas into thicker ice, thereby risking damage.

Good communications, defined responsibilities and adherence to well thought out procedures are extremely important to the safe execution of large tanker escort operations.

6.2 Tug Support in Ice

The subject of tug assistance on arrival and departure to and from terminals and offshore facilities, as well as any assistance and ice-management during loading/offloading operations, is highly dependent on various local factors. The following information is provided for general guidance only.

When a tug assists a ship during its arrival to, or departure from, an area with ice, there is a risk of collision, particularly when towlines are used. For example, the tug may encounter an area with many ice floes and become stuck (see Figure 11). To avoid collision in such situations, the tug Master should constantly make sure that the assisted ship is ready to go astern and manoeuvre in such a way that a collision can be avoided. It is also important to make sure that the towline does not slacken and pick up ice, which could result in an increased risk of it parting.

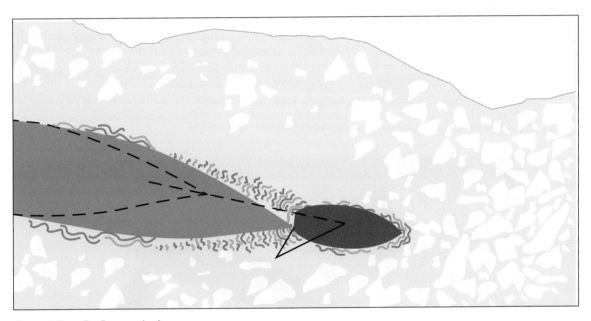

Figure 11: Escort Tug Encountering Ice

Considering the above, it is important that great care is taken during towing operations. In addition, the speed must be lower than in the case of towing in areas with no ice. The safest approach is to use the tug to push, to break ice or to remove ice between the jetty and the assisted ship.

6.2.1 Arrival at Jetty

Experience shows that the best way to bring a ship alongside a jetty in areas with ice is to manoeuvre the ship parallel to the jetty and as close to it as safely possible (see Figure 12), ensuring that there is a minimum of ice between the jetty and the ship and that the ice on the seaward side pushes the bow towards the jetty. However, this approach is rarely feasible and, as a general rule, it should always be expected that there will be ice between the jetty and the assisted ship.

Figure 12 shows a ship assisted by a tug using a towline attached to the ship's bow. In positions 1 and 2, the bow of the assisted ship is towed as close to the jetty as possible; the tug places the bow of the ship at an angle of about 45 degrees to the jetty and slides towards the jetty, ensuring that there is no ice in front of the assisted ship (position 3). If this manoeuvre fails and there is too much ice between the jetty and the ship, the procedure shown in Figure 13 should be applied.

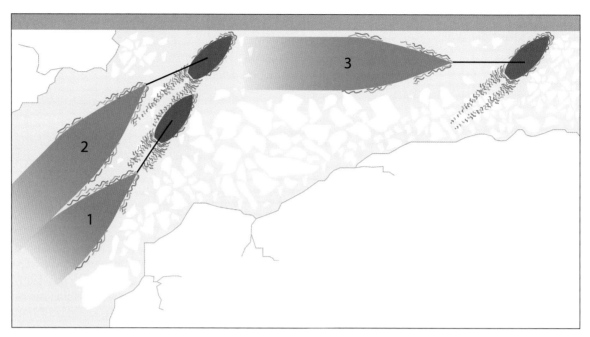

Figure 12: Tug Assisting Ship to Berth

In Figure 13, the assisted ship and tug A have fastened a spring line ashore. Tug A moves forward in relation to the spring line, flushing the ice between the ship and the jetty astern, which makes it possible for the assisted ship to proceed carefully on its spring line, bringing its bow to the jetty. It should be ensured that the ship's crew are aware of the particular risks associated with this manoeuvre. The assisted ship can then move its stern alternately towards and away from the jetty, pumping away the ice between the jetty and the ship. Tug A can sail to the side of the ship to push on it, or it may sail to another position (e.g. B or C) to push or help in removing the ice between the ship and the jetty.

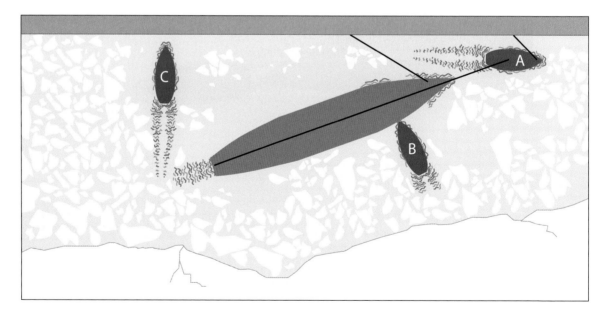

Figure 13: Using a Tug to Clear Ice from Jetty Face

Tugs B and C in Figure 13 depict how several tugs can be used. Tug B pushes at the bow in order to bring it alongside the jetty, while tug C assists in removing the ice between the ship and the jetty.

In some cases it is possible to use a tug between the ship and the jetty to push away ice by means of the tug's propeller wash. A pre-condition for such a manoeuvre is that other tugs are ready to keep the assisted ship away from the jetty while the ice is being removed, since there is a risk that the assisted ship may make contact with the tug.

6.2.2 Departure from Jetty

Before a ship leaves the jetty it is important that the tugs break the ice in an adequate area around it, so that the assisted ship is able to move as freely as possible in the ice (Figure 14).

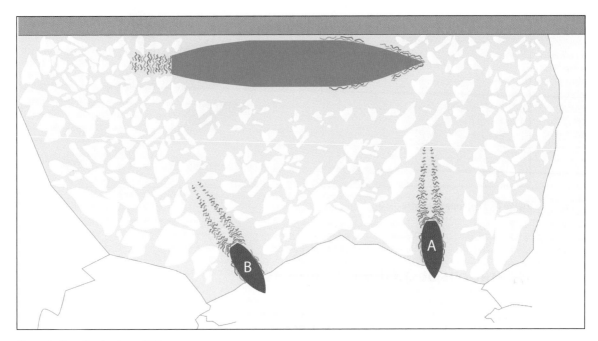

Figure 14: Tugs Clearing Ice to Aid Departure

When the ice has been broken around the ship, the tug(s) should attach towlines to the ship and pull it away from the jetty (Figure 15) to make room for manoeuvring the two tugs in between the jetty and the ship. It is important to pay attention to ensuring that the assisted ship does not drift back towards the jetty before the tugs are in a position where they can used for pushing (see Figure 16).

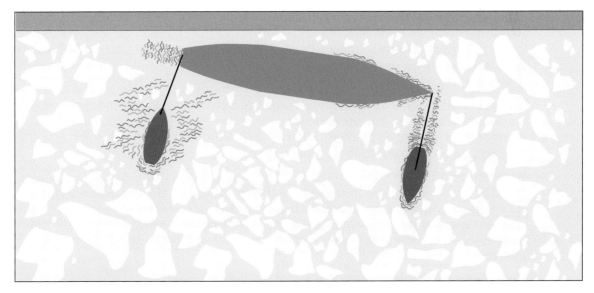

Figure 15: Moving-off from Jetty

If a ship is to be turned in a harbour basin, the ice around the ship must be in constant movement, since the ice will otherwise form blocks at the bow and the quarter. The ice can be kept in constant movement by a tug working in the ice around the ship, particularly at the bow and quarter (see Figure 16).

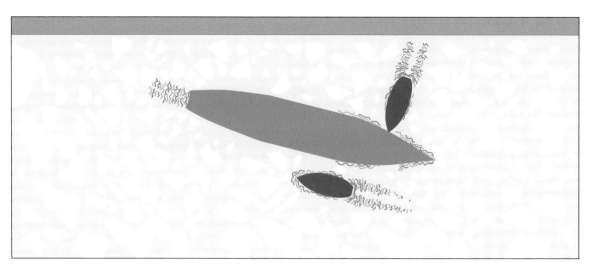

Figure 16: Departure from Jetty

6.3 Operations at Offshore Terminals

6.3.1 *Approach*

The approach to an offshore terminal during the ice season is normally made with the assistance of icebreakers. As part of the overall operation it is important to schedule the arrival of the tanker, and operations at the terminal, so that ships do not have to wait in ice.

The transition between normal icebreaker escort, and icebreaker-assisted approach to a terminal installation is characterised by the breaking of a more extensive area of ice to allow the tanker to manoeuvre to the terminal. This may be accomplished by one or two of the icebreaker escort vessels, or by a dedicated icebreaking tug provided by the terminal for that purpose. Ice should be broken in the approach area to the terminal and in areas that are 'up-ice' from the terminal, i.e in a direction such that only brash ice, rather than close packed ice, will drift into the terminal and approach area. This icebreaking should be accomplished before the tanker approaches the terminal berthing area.

In all cases, the direction of drift of the ice floe is critical to the decision of where to break ice. Ice will drift, and may pack, under the influence of wind, current and tide experienced at the site and elsewhere. Ice may drift in a different direction to a ship exposed to the same influences. Therefore, the optimum direction for the ship to approach the mooring will be influenced by the expected ice drift, as well as the normal considerations of wind, tide, current and proximity to navigational hazards.

Should tug assistance be required to moor to the terminal (jetty or single point mooring structure), such tugs should be capable of sustained operations in the maximum thickness of ice that is forecast to be encountered at the terminal. Special care should be taken to prevent loss of control of the tanker, and subsequent collision between tanker and tug or terminal, caused by the tug coming fast in ice while assisting the tanker to berth. Towlines should be under some tension at all times to prevent the towline dragging in the ice, abrading and parting.

Specific procedures to avoid heavy ice contact of hoses and moorings should be developed and employed. This is particularly true of single point mooring arrangements, where specialised bow moorings may be employed.

(Courtesy © Arno Keinonen)

Figure 17: Ice Management Vessels at an Offshore Terminal

6.3.2 Operations Alongside

Icebreaking operations 'up-ice' should continue throughout the period that the tanker is moored to the terminal. This can be accomplished by icebreakers, or by a dedicated icebreaking tug. For single point mooring terminals, a tug may be stationed astern of the tanker to assist with position keeping. If so, the tug should assist in keeping the ship's head pointing 'up-ice', rather than into wind or tide, to minimise the ice forces on the tanker. The towline used should be kept clear of the ice. The direction of ice drift should be monitored at all times, particularly if a change in climatic conditions causes a change in drift which may trap the tanker at the terminal when ice drift direction changes. This is particularly important if the tanker is moored to an offshore jetty structure, where the tanker could be 'beset' by the ice and damaged or forced off the berth by drifting ice. The operational procedures at such a terminal should allow for early departure of the tanker if a danger of besetting arises.

6.3.3 Departure

The additional area of ice required for the tanker to manoeuvre from the terminal towards and into the departure channel should be broken prior to unmooring. Specific procedures are required to avoid contact between ice and terminal and tanker equipment (hoses, moorings) to prevent damage. Otherwise, the precautions for departure mirror those of arrival.

The Use of Large Tankers in Seasonal First-Year Ice and Severe Sub-Zero Conditions

Oil Spill Response in Ice

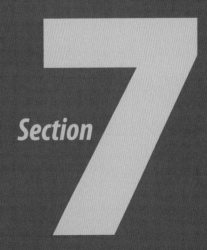

The scope of the Shipboard Oil Pollution Emergency Plan (SOPEP) of tankers operating in ice should address specific issues associated with the response to oil spills in such conditions. Operators should demonstrate that attention has been paid to the unique hazards posed by spills in the extreme cold or in ice

Oil spilled in, on and under ice offers unique challenges versus open water spills. Ice may act as a natural barrier and prevent the oil from spreading. Oil spilled on ice will usually be contained in a small area. The actual amount of spreading will be dependent on the air temperature, density and viscosity of the oil spilled and snow cover. Snow is an excellent sorbent. Oil spilled under the ice may be contained in a very restricted area that is influenced by the under-water ice roughness and currents. The spread of oil in broken ice is a function of ice concentration, wind and currents.

The primary clean-up technique for oil in ice environments is mechanical containment and recovery, either by heavy equipment or traditional spill response equipment. In broken ice conditions, traditional open water mechanical containment and recovery systems can be used with the noted caution that most oil spill booms cannot withstand the forces encountered when operating in heavy ice conditions.

The secondary option, although in some circumstances this can be the primary option, that works well in both solid ice and broken ice conditions is in-situ burning. This requires minimal logistics and provides high removal rates. Cautions associated with burning relate to the risk of unwanted fires and detrimental effects on the environment caused by the smoke plume and residues of burning.

The use of dispersants has potential in ice-covered waters. Modern technology has improved knowledge on how and when to use dispersants as part of an environmentally efficient solution for oil spills in ice covered areas.

Recent studies have considered:

- The effectiveness of dispersants and defined the 'window of opportunity' for operational use of dispersants under Arctic conditions

- existing application equipment and suggested improvements and adaptation to cold conditions and presence of ice.

The most critical parameters for obtaining an effective dispersants operation are:

- Good application of dispersant on the oil

- sufficient energy for the dispersion process, using propeller wash to assist

- oil properties at low temperature – weathering

- dispersant performance and properties under relevant conditions (salinity, temperature, oil type).

It should be noted that both the use of dispersants and in-situ burning as response techniques will require pre-approval from the relevant authorities.

Information on projects associated with oil spill response in ice may be found at:
www.mms.gov/tarprojects/476.htm
www.sintef.no/Projectweb/JIP-Oil-In-Ice/Program-overview/

The Use of Large Tankers in Seasonal First-Year Ice and Severe Sub-Zero Conditions

Proficiency of Ship's Crew

Section **8**

The safe operation of a ship trading in ice requires skill and technical proficiency in excess of those required during normal operating conditions. It is, therefore, important that suitable training is offered to complement existing experience.

All ship's officers and crew should be adequately trained for circumstances likely to be encountered when operating in low temperatures, undertaking ice navigation and/or icebreaker escort. This may take the form of in-service training, simulator training and/or Computer Based Training (CBT) and should include cold weather survival.

The following provides an example outline content to form the basis of an ice operations training course.

- Types of ice, its formation and properties
- ice regulations
- technical aspects of ice class and 'winterisation' notations, design and construction
- ship performance in ice and cold climates
- ice broadcasts and ice charts
- passage planning considerations for ice
- operating, navigating and ship handling in ice
- icebreaker operations
- berthing and mooring operations in ice
- risk assessment
- contingency planning and emergency response
- cargo and ballast operations in cold weather
- environmental issues
- limitations of shore support
- simulator module.

Masters, officers in charge of a navigational watch and officers in charge of an engineering watch should have relevant experience and training with regard to operating ships in ice and severe sub-zero conditions.

When reviewing the experience and training of ship's officers, it is preferred that experience is gained in the rank that they are serving onboard, although it is recognised that this is not always achievable.

(Courtesy © Arno Keinonen)

Figure 18: Sea Fog